Sex Lives of Animals Without Backbones

Sex Lives of Animals Without Backbones

HAIG H. NAJARIAN

ILLUSTRATED WITH DRAWINGS

CHARLES SCRIBNER'S SONS · NEW YORK

Copyright © 1976 Haig H. Najarian

Library of Congress Cataloging in Publication Data

Najarian, Haig Hagop, 1925–
  Sex lives of animals without backbones.

  Bibliography: p. 111
  Includes index.
  1. Invertebrates—Reproduction. 2. Sex
(Biology) I. Title. [DNLM: 1. Invertebrates.
2. Sex behavior, Animal. QL362 N162s]
QL364.N34   592'.01'6   75–44447
ISBN 0–684–14613–4

1 3 5 7 9 11 13 15 17 19 H/C 20 18 16 14 12 10 8 6 4 2

PRINTED IN THE UNITED STATES OF AMERICA

TO MY MOTHER
Antaram S. Najarian

Contents

Preface

THERE are relatively few people today who do not know how higher animals reproduce. It was not always this way. Earlier in history, people thought that at least some animals arose out of such things as mud and decaying material. In the middle of the seventeenth century and again during the last century, it was finally demonstrated that living things on earth arise only from other living creatures of the same kind, or species. This principle is summarized in Latin as *omne vivum ex viva*, all life comes from other life. It is the essential statement of reproduction.

The phenomenon of reproduction is a prime characteristic and function of all living things, but most people are not familiar with the reproductive processes of non-backboned animals (invertebrates). The average person would find it difficult to explain how a sponge, earthworm, or leech reproduces. A neighbor once asked about clams. He had been eating them for years and had always been bothered by the fact that the shell ought to get in the way of any reproductive process. How fascinated he was to learn how it was accomplished!

The purpose of this book is to direct attention to the various ways in which non-backboned animals reproduce. It is intended primarily for the general reader, and also

for students who are not always aware of the vast possi-
bilities invertebrate animals present in experimental study
of life processes. There is no attempt to be definitive or
exhaustive, but rather to point out the array of styles,
processes, and behavior associated with reproduction in a
clear, readable, and interesting way.

The book begins by discussing the general features of
invertebrates, with a brief review of both familiar and uncommon groups. The chapters that follow explain the
various ways in which these animals reproduce.

The illustrations, which are mostly composites of line
drawings and photographs from the literature, were exe-
cuted by Martha Miles Gordon and Marjorie Babine
Shaw.

Appreciation is extended to the Research Committee
of the University of Maine at Portland-Gorham for funds
to help with illustration costs, and to Mildred Babine who
typed drafts of the manuscript.

Sex Lives of
Animals Without
Backbones

1 What Is an Invertebrate Animal?

THE separation of animals into the categories vertebrate, having a backbone, and invertebrate, not having one, is an arbitrary division and could be made in many other ways: birds and non-birds, fish and non-fish, insects and non-insects. Biology, along with other disciplines, has developed from and depended on a dualistic way of looking at things. But this contrasting of two clear-cut poles or opposites has created many difficulties, and for some time intelligent people have accepted the idea that most conditions, situations, or ideas are on a continuum, and therefore have relative value.

Although the invertebrate-vertebrate distinction separates two categories of animals—one having a positive character and the other a negative one—it really does not reveal what an invertebrate is. To know that fish, frogs, snakes, birds, and rodents are vertebrates would indicate that they all have a backbone, but it certainly would not give information regarding the anatomy, life processes, and behavior of these animals. So too invertebrate animals are vastly different in size, structural make-up, and means of accomplishing life functions.

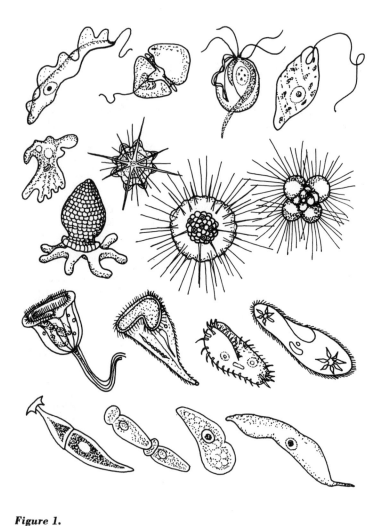

Figure 1.

Protozoans. Various single-celled organisms. Top row, flagellates; second row, naked and shelled amoebae; third row, ciliates; bottom row, sporozoans.

There are over a million kinds (species) of animals, and more than 90 percent are of the non-backboned type. Although many of the invertebrates are familiar to the average person (especially if he eats them), most go unnoticed. This is perhaps because invertebrates do not generally resemble the human animal, are not usually befriended or made pets of, and do not work (in the usual sense) for people. Compared to vertebrates, they are very small and generally dwell in habitats not shared by people. Nevertheless, the invertebrate's survival needs are as impelling as are those of the human creature or any other vertebrate.

Since the various groups of invertebrates are more dissimilar than similar, it should be helpful to characterize most of the well-known and less familiar groups before dealing with their methods of reproduction.

Protozoans are minute organisms that live either in an aquatic environment, or as parasites of other animals and plants. Because they cannot usually be seen without a microscope, they are unfamiliar to most people.

There are about 30,000 species of protozoans, referred to as flagellates, ciliates, amoebae, or sporozoans, depending on their means of locomotion (or lack of it). They are single-celled, although in many cases they exist as aggregates or colonies of cells. They are very diverse, ranging from plantlike organisms which photosynthesize, to animallike species with mouths that eat particles of food. It is interesting that not only do these single-celled organisms reproduce in a variety of ways, but many undergo sexual reproduction, something most people would not associate with microscopic creatures.

Sponges number about 5,000 species, and most of them resemble plants on gross appearance. Perhaps this is because the part usually seen is the sponge skeleton. Most are marine and are attached to some object.

Sponges are covered with microscopic surface pores and depend on a stream of water which is pulled into these pores and then expelled through larger openings on the surface. Of varying complexity, sponge bodies have chambers and canals; although they are multicellular, these cells are loose aggregates and are not organized into fixed tissues. A cell type common to all sponges is a flagellated cell (the choanocyte). Sponges reproduce either asexually or sexually and have great capacity to regenerate lost parts.

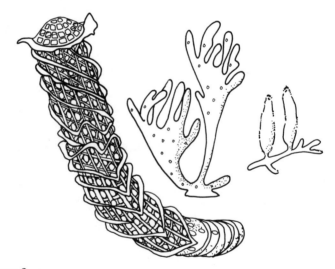

Figure 2.
Sponges. All have porous bodies and various kinds of skeletal elements.

Coelenterates are an aquatic group of animals of about 10,000 species and include the familiar jellyfishes, corals, and anemones. They are mostly a marine group whose bodies are organized into tissue layers. The single opening of the body is the mouth, and it is usually surrounded by tentacles. Many coelenterates exhibit remarkable changes in body form (polymorphism) in the various stages of their life cycles.

All species have in common a cell type, the cnidoblast. The stinging capsule is one of the many variations of this cell; there are other types which assist in food capturing and defense. Most coelenterates reproduce both sexually and asexually and also have the capacity for regeneration of parts.

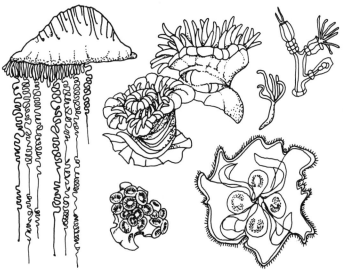

Figure 3.
Coelenterates. A diverse group of individual or colonial organisms, including jellyfish, anemones, corals, and hydroids.

Ctenophores are a group of less than a hundred species of jellylike sea animals organized on the tissue level. They somewhat resemble the jellyfish type of coelenterate, but they lack cnidoblasts and are generally not familiar to the average person unless their striking luminescence is seen on the tide at night. They are commonly called sea goose-berries, sea walnuts, or comb jellies, and most species have tentacles that are longer than the body of the animal. On these tentacles are a type of cell peculiar to ctenophores, the colloblast. The cell secretes a sticky material which assists in capturing prey. Ctenophores reproduce by sexual means only.

Figure 4.
A type of ctenophore or sea gooseberry.

Platyhelminthes are usually referred to as flatworms. There are about 15,000 species. The body has many tissues organized into functional organs, even though there is no body cavity, or coelom. One subgroup, the turbellarians (which includes the common planarians), is mostly free-living; the other two subgroups, the trematodes or flukes, and the cestodes or tapeworms, are entirely parasitic.

Although turbellarians have relatively simple life cycles,

those of flukes and tapeworms are among the most remarkable known. Most flatworms are hermaphroditic (having
both male and female sex organs in the same animal).
Although sexual reproduction is the rule, some species
can also reproduce asexually. Some forms also have superb
powers of regeneration.

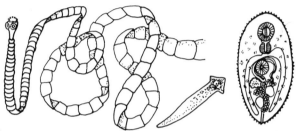

Figure 5.
*Platyhelminthes or flatworms. A tapeworm on the left, a
planarian in the middle, and a fluke on the right.*

Nemerteans or ribbon worms include about 600 species
of mostly marine worms having an extreme size range—
from a fraction of an inch to several feet in length. They

Figure 6.
*Nemerteans or ribbon worms. Each has an eversible proboscis
at the head end.*

have flat bodies and no body cavity. Characteristic of the group is a prominent proboscis which can either rest inside a fluid-filled sac or be everted. The proboscis may be much longer than the body of the worm and may have stylets at its tip. This structure aids in food capture and as a defense mechanism. Nemerteans are either male or female and reproduce sexually, although many of the larger worms can reproduce asexually too.

Rotifers are among the smallest multicellular animals on earth. They are a mostly microscopic freshwater group of about 1500 species and are characterized by a ciliated wheellike apparatus at the front end. This structure serves to sweep small organisms into the mouth of the animal. Rotifers also have an eversible, muscular pharynx (with teeth) that grinds up food material.

These animals have a most interesting reproductive pattern. In some species, females always produce more females; in other species, female rotifers produce both males and females, depending on which kinds of eggs are laid at different seasons.

Figure 7.

Rotifers. These mostly microscopic animals have a wheellike apparatus at the head end.

Gastrotrichs are small aquatic animals similar to rotifers in size and shape but lacking the wheellike apparatus at the front end and the toothed pharynx. There are about 150 species. The marine species are either male or female, but since the male gonads are incompletely developed, the females usually reproduce without the requirement of a male. Some freshwater gastrotrichs, like some rotifers, lay different kinds of eggs.

Figure 8.

Gastrotrichs. These animals are similar to rotifers in size and reproductive habits.

Nematodes, or roundworms, include over 10,000 species of unsegmented, cylindrical worms that are second only to insects in abundance. Although many are parasitic in other animals and plants, most species are free-living in soil or water. They range in size from a fraction of an inch to several feet in length. A few species are hermaphroditic but most reproduce sexually. The male is usually much smaller than the female.

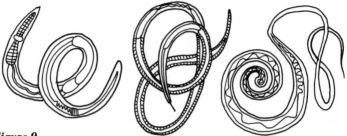

Figure 9.

Nematodes or roundworms. These animals are very abundant in soil or water, and, as parasites, many cause serious human ailments.

Nematomorphans, or horsehair worms, are a small group (about 250 species) of slender, cylindrical animals. The adults are free-living in fresh water, but the larvae live as parasites, mostly in insects. The males and females copulate, and the female then lays long strings of eggs. After hatching, the larvae are either eaten by or penetrate such insects as crickets, grasshoppers, or roaches. The larvae later emerge from the insects and develop into adult worms.

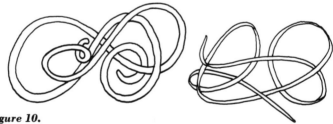

Figure 10.

Nematomorphan worms. The adults are very thin and usually have a tangled appearance.

A feature peculiar to these animals is that the reproductive ducts discharge the sex cells through the intestinal opening.

Bryozoans are minute mosslike animals that are mostly marine. There are about 4000 species, living mostly as attached colonies of individuals. The bryozoan has an exterior encasement and it captures food particles in tentacles which project from folds around the mouth. Most species are hermaphroditic, and there is a variety of both sexual and asexual ways in which they reproduce.

Figure 11.
Three colonies of bryozoans. These mosslike animals are all aquatic.

Mollusks include about 120,000 species and are the most familiar group of invertebrate animals. Among them are such organisms as clams, snails, slugs, oysters, squid, and octopuses. They exist in all aquatic environments and some live on land. Although most mollusks are either male or

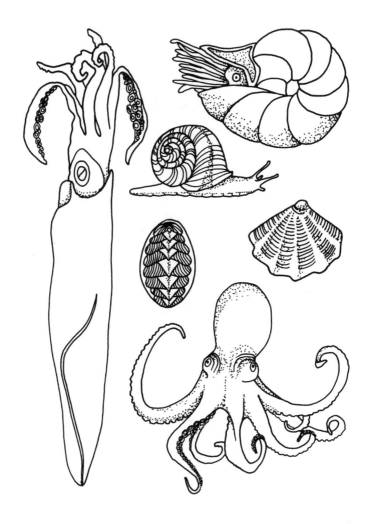

Figure 12.

Mollusks. This abundant group, comprised of many species, includes squids, chitons, clams, nautiluses, snails, and octopuses.

female and reproduce sexually, there are interesting variations in their reproductive behavior. Some animals reverse sex, some shoot stimulant darts at each other, and some lose an arm while mating.

Annelids are a 9000-species group of segmented worms. They are very diverse and abundant and include land, freshwater, and marine animals. The mode of reproduction varies but includes both sexual and asexual means. Many are hermaphroditic, although they generally are not self-fertilizing.

Figure 13.

Annelids or segmented worms. This diverse group includes earthworms, leeches, and clamworms.

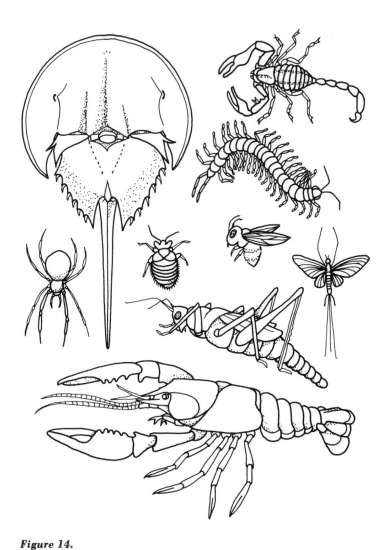

Figure 14.

Arthropods. This most diverse and abundant group of animals includes scorpions, centipedes, spiders, insects, and crayfish.

Arthropods are the most abundant animals on earth. There are over 800,000 species, characterized by a segmented body, jointed appendages, and an exterior skeleton. Arthropods are familiar to people because they include such varied creatures as lobsters, spiders, mosquitoes, scorpions, and shrimp.

Most arthropods have separate sexes and reproduce sexually by copulation, although there are some females which can produce offspring without males. The arthropods exhibit interesting mating behavior.

Echinoderms are a marine group of about 6000 species, which include such organisms as starfish, sea urchins, sand

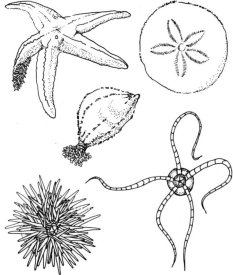

Figure 15.
Echinoderms. A marine group of animals that includes starfish, brittle stars, sea cucumbers, sand dollars, and sea urchins.

dollars, and sea cucumbers. Their body symmetry is radial; that of most other invertebrates is bilateral. Although a few echinoderms are hermaphroditic, most are either male or female and reproduce sexually without copulation. They generally have great capacity to regenerate, and many reproduce asexually by the regeneration of whole animals from parts.

There are about a dozen other groups of invertebrates that are not mentioned here, partly because they include relatively few species, and partly because they reproduce in a manner similar to the groups that are reviewed. Those that have interesting varieties of reproductive behavior are described in Chapters 5 and 6.

2 What Is Reproduction?

ALTHOUGH the continuation of life depends on reproduction, the word may mean different things to different people. In this book the term is used for the way (or ways) that animal species produce offspring. Cell division in multicellular animals, whereby individual cells produce similar or dissimilar cells, may be considered a reproductive process, but is not treated as such here—unless this division results in the production of a new whole animal, as in the unicellular organisms. Reproduction is not synonymous with the mating of males and females, even though it is generally held to be, and it is most often thought of as occurring sexually or asexually. It would be more accurate to state that reproduction in invertebrate animals is accomplished in a variety of ways, but for the sake of the dualistic convention, the various forms of reproduction can be considered as either asexual or sexual, though there is not always a clear-cut distinction between the two. In fact, even the sex of some invertebrates is not fixed and can be influenced or reversed by a variety of factors.

In asexual reproduction, only one parent is involved, and no gametes or sex cells are produced. Nevertheless offspring are produced in a variety of ways, and even though they may sometimes look different from the parent, their genetic endowment is entirely that of the parent. The asexually-reproducing animal can be considered theoretically immortal because the animal transmits its entire stock of hereditary traits to its offspring.

In sexual reproduction, there are usually two parents, and the offspring result from a combination of parental gametes. The exception to this is the female invertebrate which produces offspring without the participation of a male. Since such females have obvious sex and produce sex cells, they are classified in the sexual group.

It is biparental sexual reproduction that produces off-spring capable of adaptive responses to changing environmental conditions; uniparental asexual reproduction usually results in offspring which are exact genetic copies of the single parent.

Although sexual reproduction is more widespread in invertebrate animals than asexual means, many groups of animals produce offspring by a combination of the two methods.

3 Asexual Reproduction

INVERTEBRATES have evolved a variety of ways of reproducing asexually, but in each case the parent animal acts alone. In some methods the parent maintains its identity, whereas in others this identity is forever lost in the reproductive process. In all cases, however, the parent undergoes degrees of differentiation, regeneration, and growth associated with asexual reproduction, either before or after the offspring have been produced. In vertebrates, asexual reproduction occurs only when identical twins are born.

Fission is perhaps the simplest kind of asexual reproduction. It takes place mostly in unicellular organisms, but modifications of the process are also found in several types

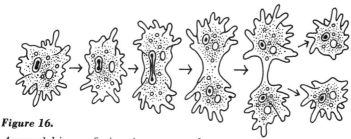

Figure 16.
Asexual binary fission in an amoeba.

21

of multicellular invertebrates. It involves the division of a single parent organism into two or more offspring, which are usually copies of the parent itself.

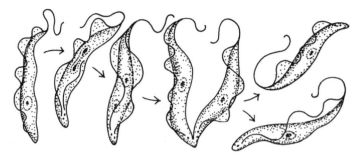

Figure 17.
Asexual longitudinal binary fission in a flagellate.

In protozoa, for example, fission is a common (but not exclusive) .manner of asexual reproduction. If the parent organism divides into two offspring about equal in size, it is called binary fission, but even here there are variations of the method, depending on the plane of division: In longitudinal binary fission (which occurs in the flagellated type

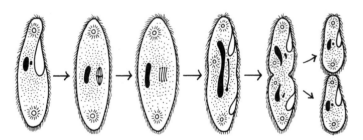

Figure 18.
Asexual transverse binary fission in a ciliate.

of protozoa), the plane of division is along the longitudinal axis of the animal. Transverse binary fission occurs in most of the ciliated kinds of protozoa and involves division across the longitudinal axis. When the divisional plane is at an angle to the body, this is called oblique binary fission.

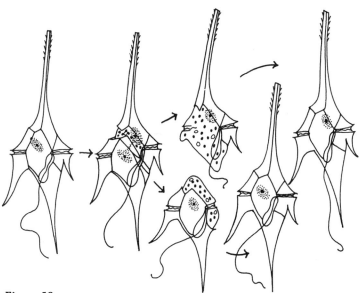

Figure 19.
Asexual oblique binary fission in a flagellate.

In some protozoa (such as parasitic sporozoans), there is a series of nuclear divisions in the parent body, but a delay in the cytoplasmic constrictions around each new nucleus. This results in a parent that is temporarily a multinucleated mass. Once the divisions are complete, however, several to very many offspring result from the original organism. The general process is called multiple fission, but there are variations in this as well. In those organisms which have both an asexual and sexual phase in their life cycles, should multiple fission occur in the asexual phase, it is called schizogony. When multiple fission follows sexual union of the organisms or their delegates in the life cycle, it is called sporogony. The offspring, called spores, have a tough-walled outer covering.

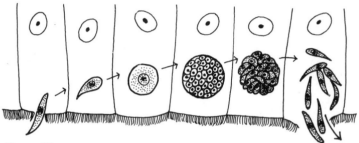

Figure 20.
Asexual multiple fission (schizogony) in a sporozoan. A single parasite enters the host cell and produces several progeny.

Why some groups of protozoans are characterized by longitudinal and others by transverse, oblique, or multiple fission is not clear. However, not only is the generation

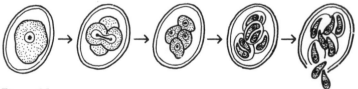

Figure 21.
Asexual multiple fission (sporogony) in a sporozoan. A single zygote produces several progeny.

span short in these asexually-reproducing animals (often less than an hour), but also organisms that reproduce by fission theoretically do not die, since an infinite number of divisions is possible if suitable environmental conditions prevail. Factors which work against their infinite increase are such things as being part of the food chain of other animals, or suffering adverse seasonal changes. In parasitic species, the immune machinery of their hosts takes care of many of their numbers.

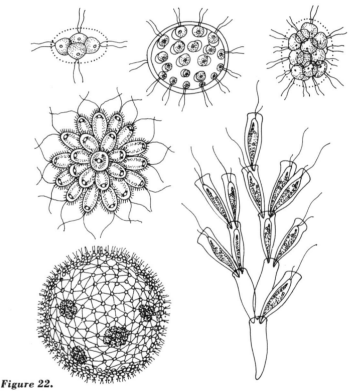

Figure 22.

Various colonies of protozoa. These colonies result when the cells do not separate after asexual fissions.

The offspring of the fission process are not always separate organisms. In many flagellates, there is either incomplete division of the protozoan body, so that a chain or group of individuals results, or the progeny stick together or are enclosed in an envelope secreted by the cells. These are referred to as colonial protozoa, and some colonies may consist of thousands of individual cells.

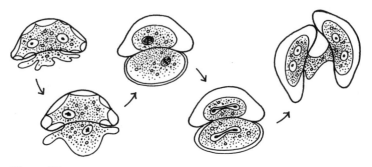

Figure 23.

Asexual binary fission in a shelled amoeba. One of the organisms secretes a shell around itself before fission is completed.

Many protozoa, especially the amoebae, have exterior shells constructed of a variety of substances (such as calcium carbonate, salts of silicon, cellulose, chitin, or sand grains). The shells are either secreted by the organisms, or are gathered from their surroundings and cemented together as a housing around the cell. This should present a problem for these organisms that reproduce asexually by fission, but they have managed in more than one way. In some cases the shell of the protozoan divides along with the body. In other instances, one of the offspring gets the old shell, and the other makes a new covering for itself. There are yet other kinds which discard the shell completely at fission, each offspring then making a new shell for itself.

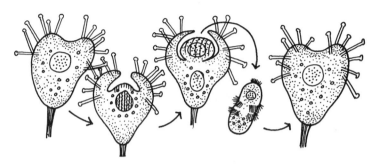

Figure 24.

Asexual internal budding in a stalked protozoan. The bud is maintained inside the parent and then released as a larva, which eventually develops into an adult form.

Some protozoans are said to reproduce by budding, but here the process is simply another modified form of fission in which the division of the body of the parent is so unequal that it gives the effect of a small individual being budded off a larger parent. These so-called buds may form either on the surface of the protozoan, or internally, where they develop and are later released from the parent.

True budding is an asexual means of reproduction characteristic of several types of invertebrates, such as sponges, coelenterates, and some worms. It is a process in which an offspring forms as a growth from the parent. The bud begins as an amorphous mass, but eventually attains the form and size of the parent from which it was derived. External buds may either detach from the parent and take

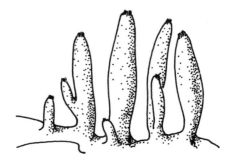

Figure 25.

Asexual external budding in a sponge colony.

up independent existence, as in the coelenterate *Hydra*, or remain attached to the parent. The latter is characteristic of animals such as sponges which live in colonies. Adult tapeworms produce buds from an area just behind the

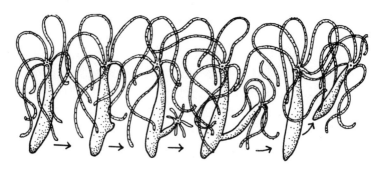

Figure 26.

Asexual external budding in Hydra. *More than one individual may bud off from the parent, but none remains attached, and hence there is no colony formation.*

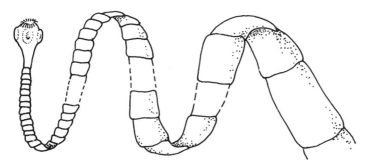

Figure 27.

Asexual external budding in a tapeworm (dotted lines indicate missing portions). The segments bud off from the region just behind the head and remain attached.

head, and each bud remains attached, eventually becoming a mature unit of the entire worm.

Many animals reproduce by a process of internal budding, in which certain cells are enveloped in a resistant covering. These buds either escape from the parent and develop into individuals similar to the parent, or they remain inside the parent's body until its death and disintegration, after which the buds develop into offspring. Internal buds do not initially resemble the parent in form or size; that development takes place at a later time.

The internal buds of freshwater sponges are called gemmules. These develop during the fall and when the parent sponge dies, the gemmules remain alive over the winter and develop into new sponges when environmental conditions are suitable in the spring. Mosslike aquatic animals called bryozoans develop internal buds similar to the gemmules of sponges. These are called statoblasts and,

like the gemmules, they develop internally in the parent
colony, swim off when the parent disintegrates, survive
adverse environmental conditions of cold and drought,

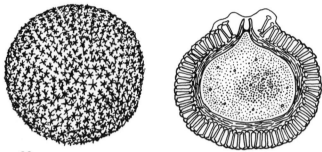

Figure 28.

*Surface view (left) and cross section (right) of gemmules, or
asexual internal buds removed from a sponge. The gemmules
develop into new individuals after the parent sponge disintegrates.*

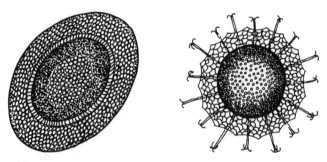

Figure 29.

*Surface view (left) and cross section (right) of statoblasts, or
asexual internal buds removed from a bryozoan. The statoblasts
function in the same way as the gemmules of sponges.*

and then later develop into new animals when conditions are favorable.

Some kinds of larval tapeworms develop offspring by extensive internal budding from a germinative tissue in their larval stages. In such cases, the head and neck of the tapeworm are the only areas developed and the rest of the complete worm must await budding at a later date when the young buds find themselves in the intestine of a suitable vertebrate host.

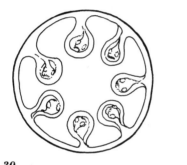 

Figure 30.
Asexual internal budding in the larval stage of a tapeworm. Several tapeworm heads have budded in the cyst on the left. An enlarged view of one head on the right.

The process of budding, whether internal or external, depends upon an animal's possessing either a multipotential cell capable of forming all the other cell types in a given animal body (as with sponges and coelenterates) or undifferentiated tissue that can develop into the constituent tissues and organs of the parent. Tapeworms and several other kinds of invertebrates have this tissue.

Budding is not that different from regeneration, a characteristic of many invertebrates and some backboned animals. Lizards have little difficulty in regenerating lost tails, and some amphibians can even regenerate limbs. Mammals (including people) can regenerate a variety of tissues, but in the more complex animals, the power to regenerate whole parts diminishes, much less the ability to produce an entirely new animal or colony.

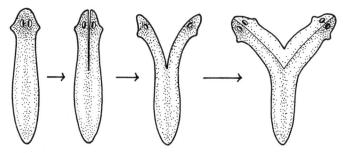

Figure 31.

Regeneration in a planaria which has been sliced down the middle of the head region.

There are a few other asexual ways in which invertebrates reproduce. These are not primary methods, but rather are induced by various environmental conditions. They include modifications of fission, budding, and regeneration.

Encystment is characteristic of many freshwater and parasitic protozoa. In this process, the organism accumulates food reserves and forms a resistant cover around itself. It also generally loses water and becomes inactive. While the primary function of encystment is not reproduction,

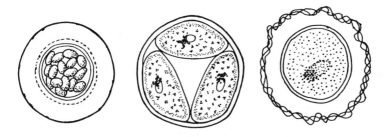

Figure 32.

Various encysted protozoans. Asexual fissions usually occur within the cyst, and progeny are released under favorable environmental conditions.

the net result is additional offspring from the parent. Although a single organism encysts, more than one offspring usually come out of the cyst when suitable environmental conditions develop. The production of offspring while the organism is in encystment or shortly after encystment is accomplished by fission, budding, and occasionally by sexual means.

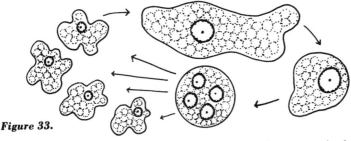

Figure 33.

This parasitic amoeba (upper center) reproduces routinely by asexual binary fission, but at times forms a cyst (lower center) from which four offspring develop.

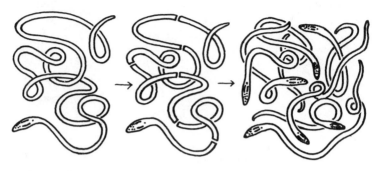

Figure 34.

Asexual fragmentation in a nemertean worm. Several off-spring have developed from the original parent.

In the process of fragmentation, the animal breaks up into several pieces, each of which will eventually regenerate into offspring similar to the parent. This occurs in a variety of animals such as anemones, sponges, turbellarians, nemerteans, and annelids.

Figure 35.

Asexual fragmentation in a sea anemone. Fragments from the basal portion of the parent eventually develop into offspring.

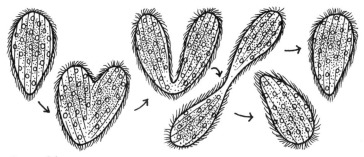

Figure 36.

Asexual plasmotomy in which a multinucleated protozoan divides into two offspring.

There are some protozoa which have many nuclei, and when such multinucleated bodies divide into several off-spring, the process is called plasmotomy.

Polyembryony or twinning can occur in both backboned and non-backboned animals. It involves the production of two or more offspring from a single fertilized egg. This

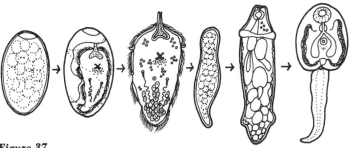

Figure 37.

Life-cycle stages of a trematode worm. Thousands of larval stages on the right develop asexually from the original egg on the left.

happens in the developmental stages, and in some insects hundreds of offspring develop from a single egg.

There are some insects, notably the gall wasp, in which the larvae actually produce more larvae. This is a special kind of asexual reproduction called paedogenesis. It can happen that in several successive generations, some of the larvae will pupate and develop into males and females, which then mate.

4 Sexual Reproduction

AMONG invertebrates there is far more to sexual reproduction than the penis of a male emitting germ cells into the genital canal of a female. Many male invertebrates do not have a penis, and in fact there are several groups which do not even have permanent gonads (ovaries and testes). Some animals fertilize eggs inside their bodies, and some outside.

Invertebrates accomplish sexual reproduction in remarkably varied ways. Offspring may result from the activities of two whole organisms acting as sex cells, from the combination of sex cells from distinct male and female animals, from a single parent having both sexes within its body, or from a female animal without the assistance of a male partner.

Temporary Union

A sexual process that occurs in all ciliated protozoa is a maneuver called conjugation. In this phenomenon, two separate organisms temporarily fuse and exchange nuclear material. Protozoa that conjugate have two types of nuclei

—a single large nucleus, and one-to-many smaller nuclei. In conjugation, the large nucleus disintegrates, and there is a series of nuclear replications in the smaller nuclei during and after temporary union of the two individuals. The essential point in this process is that from each protozoan a portion of the small nucleus migrates to the other partner and enters into its nuclear make-up.

Members of a species will not conjugate with all other members of the same species but only with certain mating types. Therefore, a degree of "maleness" and "femaleness" is present in these single-celled organisms. Although it is fission that actually produces several new bodies from a conjugating pair, the temporary union of the two indi-

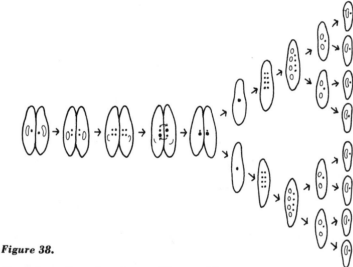

Figure 38.

Sexual conjugation in a ciliate with temporary union and nuclear exchange between the two protozoans. By means of fission, eight progeny develop from the original conjugating pair on the left.

viduals is a sexual method, because it results in offspring which have a combination of hereditary traits from two parents.

Self-Fertilization

Conjugation requires partners, but there also exists in ciliates a process called autogamy in which no partners are needed. Autogamy results in recombinations of genetic material within an individual. In a sense, such a protozoan may be considered a hermaphroditic animal.

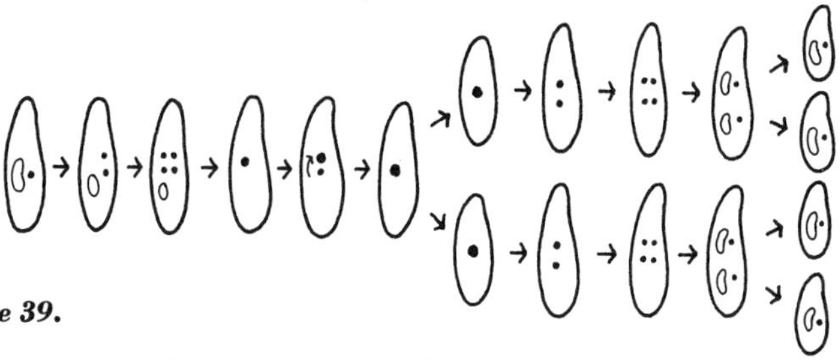

Figure 39.

Autogamy or self-mating in a ciliate. Genetic recombination occurs in a single individual, and four progeny result from fission.

Permanent Union

In this form of sexual reproduction, there is either complete union of two organisms acting as gametes or sex cells, or the union of gametes produced by male and female animals. Multicellular animals have certain areas or organs which produce gametes. Among the unicellular protozoans, however, there are instances where entire animals behave as sex cells, fusing not only their bodies but also their

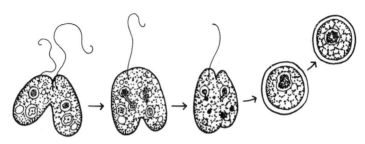

Figure 40.

Hologamy in a flagellate in which the bodies of the protozoans act as sex cells. Progeny develop later by asexual fission of the zygote on the right.

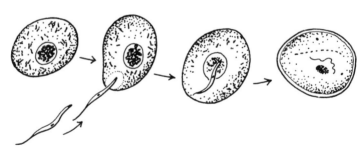

Figure 41.

Sexual reproduction in a coccidian. The thin active sperm fertilizes the larger ovum, and the resulting zygote on the right will produce many progeny by asexual fissions.

nuclei. This process is called hologamy. The only way to distinguish the organisms that act as sex cells is in their behavior; in all other respects they resemble the nonsexual forms of the species.

In other cases, the organisms which act as sex cells differ in size to a varying extent. When the size difference is extreme, the small, thin, motile cells are called sperm, and the large, non-motile ones, ova, or eggs. The fertilized ova are called zygotes. In protozoa, zygotes develop directly into offspring, or they form a cover around themselves and reproduce further by asexual fission.

It is difficult to think of a whole organism performing as a sex cell, and perhaps even stranger to think of sperm and eggs in unicellular organisms, because this sexual functioning is so different from that of backboned animals, which are more familiar.

While theoretically there is no death of organisms that reproduce by asexual fission, those in which the entire body acts as a sex cell immediately lose their identity. Even in those animals which use delegates or gametes in sexual reproduction, the delegates lose their body form. In both these kinds of sexual union, however, the progeny are eventually similar to the parents, even though many in transient larval stages are quite different from the parents that produced them.

Before considering the various aspects and modifications of sexual reproduction in non-backboned animals, it is useful to consider briefly the basic process in backboned animals, or vertebrates. The more familiar vertebrate groups can serve as comparison for the extremely varied and often striking aspects of sexual reproduction in non-backboned animals.

Sexual Reproduction in Vertebrates

Vertebrates include the fishes, amphibians, reptiles, birds, and mammals, and all are either male or female (although sex reversal is possible in some). They have permanent gonads (ovaries and testes), which may become extremely large and active during certain seasons of the year. In order for reproduction to take place, males and females of each species must first attract each other and recognize that they are of the same species. Vertebrates use a variety of signals in sexual attraction, recognition, and mating; they depend on odor, sound, sight, and behavioral cues. Some vertebrates rely primarily on one of these signals; most use a combination of them.

Fish generally reproduce externally, shedding sperm and eggs into open water, where fertilization and development of the eggs occur. The process is called spawning. Although there is usually no copulation, the males of some fish, such as sharks and their relatives, are equipped for a modified type of sexual mating. Devices called "claspers" act as a groove for the passage of sperm into the female, and development of the young takes place within the female.

The eggs of frogs and toads are also fertilized externally in water, but a kind of copulation does take place, even though the males of these animals lack a penis. The male mounts the female and with his swollen thumb pads strokes her belly until she releases eggs from her hind opening. He then releases sperm from his hind opening, and the eggs are fertilized in the water. This is a copulatory act, although fertilization does not take place within the female. (If the belly of a receptive male frog is stroked, the frog will regard the human finger as a substitute female

Figure 42.

Breeding activities in vertebrates: fish and frogs spawning, sharks and cats copulating, and birds in a "cloacal kiss."

and grasp it with much enthusiasm.) Frogs develop entirely within water.

Salamanders undergo internal fertilization, but there is also no true copulation. The male salamander releases packages of sperm (spermatophores) into the water. The female draws them into her hind opening, and they are stored inside her. The eggs are fertilized as they come down her genital ducts and are laid in water where they eventually develop into young.

Turtles and crocodiles copulate, the males having an erectile penis with an open groove which transports sperm to the female. In these and other reptiles, such as snakes, the fertilized eggs, with shells, may be laid externally or be retained within the mother, who later gives birth to the young.

While male birds usually do not have a penis, birds mate sexually by placing their cloacal openings together. Sperm is released into the female who later lays shelled eggs which are incubated externally until they hatch. Some birds, such as ostriches and ducks, do have a small penis that is used in copulation, but the fertilized eggs of these species are also incubated outside the female's body.

Among mammals, all males have a penis, a closed tube which transports sperm into the female. The penis has erectile tissue, gets engorged with blood, and is thus rigid. (In some species, including dogs and cats, the penis has a bone; in some whales this bone is several feet long.) Complete development of the young takes place in the female, except for a few egg-laying mammals and the marsupials, such as the kangaroo, which carry around their young in a pouch for some time after birth.

5 Sexual Reproduction in Invertebrates

INVERTEBRATES exhibit great diversity in their reproductive machinery, sexual behavior, and breeding patterns.

Sex Cells

Most invertebrates produce gametes, or sex cells, from permanent gonads. Many animals which lack such structures nevertheless possess functional sperm and ova. Where does this reproductive material come from? In animals such as sponges and some coelenterates, it develops from certain cell types within the body. In other animals, gametes may develop from an internal sheet of undifferentiated tissue; even gonads may actually develop on a seasonal basis. Among the animals which have this tissue are many types broadly referred to as worms.

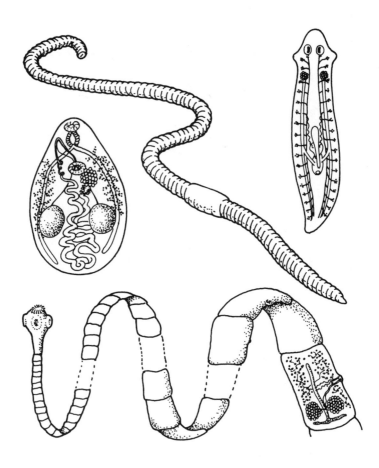

Figure 43.

*Hermaphroditic invertebrates having permanent male and
female gonads: (clockwise from upper right) planarian, tapeworm, trematode, and earthworm.*

Double Sex

Except for the arthropods (made up mostly of insects), almost all groups of invertebrates include some species in which both sexes are present in the same animal. This hermaphroditism—the ability of a single animal to produce both eggs and sperm—exists in most sponges, many coelenterates, ctenophores, most flukes, tapeworms, most annelids, some mollusks (snails, oysters, clams), and barnacles. Even though each animal is both male and female, most do not self-fertilize but rather mate with others of their species.

Sex Switching

Another example of the sexual diversity of invertebrates is the condition called protandry, a kind of sex switching in which the same gonad produces first sperm and then eggs. This occurs in some species of oysters, clams, sea cucumbers, brittle stars, and bryozoans. Whether such animals are functional males or females depends on the time factor.

Sexual Dimorphism

Among vertebrates, when there is a noticeable size difference between males and females of a given species, the male is usually larger than the female. When size diffences occur in non-backboned animals, the males are usually considerably smaller than the females, some being appendages or tenants of the female.

Some female brittle stars have dwarf males attached to their mouths. In one species of echiurid of the sea, a female several feet long keeps her male mate, of less than an inch in length, inside her kidney. In a nematode that is parasitic in the urinary tract of rats, the female worm keeps her male mate inside her vagina. There are female barnacles that have dwarf males living permanently inside them. In such cases of extreme sexual dimorphism one can think of the animals as hermaphrodites; certainly the males of the species are little more than a gonad.

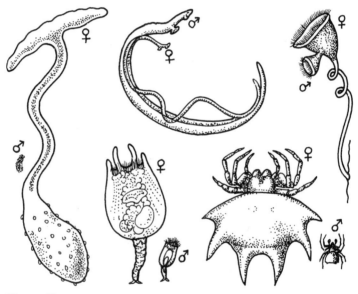

Figure 44.

Sexual dimorphism in some invertebrates. The male (♂) is usually smaller than or of different shape from the female (♀). (Clockwise from the left)—echiurid worms, schistosome worms, a protozoan ciliate, spiders, and rotifers.

Virgin Birth

Although it is not a widespread phenomenon, the off-spring of some invertebrates develop from unfertilized eggs laid by the female, the male taking no part in it. This is called parthenogenesis, or virgin birth, and occurs in some species of rotifers, gastrotrichs, nematodes, and such insects as bees and aphids. Parthenogenetic activity occurs only at certain times or under certain conditions. At other times in their life cycles, the females may produce offspring from eggs which have been fertilized.

Among honeybees, for example, parthenogenetic activity is the business of the queen bee who copulates with males just once in her life, storing sperm in a sac inside her body. By means of valves on this sac, she controls the fertilization of her eggs. Fertilized eggs become other females (workers or queens), and unfertilized eggs become males or drones.

Release of Sex Cells

Sometimes a combination of environmental conditions (such as light and temperature) seems to stimulate the release of gametes in invertebrates; in other cases, emission of sex cells stimulates a partner's reciprocal emission. In starfish the release of eggs or sperm stimulates the opposite sex to release its sperm or eggs. In the clamworm, the male emits sperm into the water, which induces the female to lay her eggs. More unusual is the case of those crustacea who depend on certain algae in their diet to stimulate the release of gametes.

Aquatic invertebrates do not always have reproductive tubes or ducts to deliver the sperm and/or eggs into water where fertilization is to occur. Although in lower invertebrates, such as jellyfish, ctenophores, and some turbellarian flatworms, the mouth of the animal serves this purpose, a commonly used conduit can be the tubes of the kidney. This is the case with some annelids, clams, and snails.

Parental Care

Whether fertilization of eggs occurs inside or outside the body, among most invertebrates there is no parental care of the developing eggs or young. However, some exceptional species do pay attention to the developing offspring, and this brooding activity can be quite varied.

In certain coelenterates and echinoderms the eggs are brooded on the tentacles or limbs of the animal until the motile larvae hatch and swim off on their own. The female crayfish attaches its eggs to abdominal appendages and broods them until they hatch. The male sea spider attaches the eggs to his appendages and broods them. Some leeches carry around their eggs which are stuck to their bodies. The female octopus guards and fans her eggs until they hatch. Female earwigs are very attentive to their eggs, licking them until the young emerge. There are invertebrates which brood the fertilized eggs inside their bodies until the young are born, partially or completely resembling the parents. This occurs in some species of turbellarians, rotifers, nematodes, leeches, clams, and chitons. There is even a species of polychaete in which the young nourish on the mother's blood vessels in a manner similar to placental mammals.

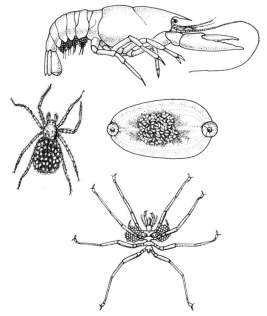

Figure 45.

Brooding and parental care in some invertebrates: (top figure) —female crayfish carrying eggs on abdominal segments; (middle figures)—female spider and hermaphroditic leech with young on backs; (bottom figure)—male sea spider brooding eggs on front appendages.

Hypodermic Sex

Leeches are a class of hermaphroditic annelids which live on land, in fresh water, and the sea. Only some of them are parasitic bloodsuckers; most are predators or scavengers, eating such things as insect larvae, crustaceans, and snails.

All species have one pair of ovaries and several pairs of testes. These gonads have ducts and accessory sexual structures which open as single male and female pores on the ventral side of the first third of the body. Even though they are hermaphroditic, leeches do not self-fertilize. In those species which have an eversible penis, there is reciprocal copulation, where the penis transfers sperm from the male opening of one leech to the female opening of the opposite partner.

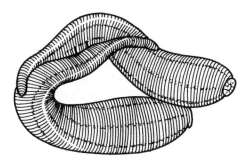

Figure 46.

Reciprocal copulation between two leeches. Although these animals are hermaphroditic, the penis of each animal transfers sperm to the partner.

Leeches lacking a penis collect the sperm internally in packets called spermatophores and then reciprocally expel these packets from the male opening into their partners' bodies. Most spermatophores have a sharp point which is driven into the partner. The sperm released from the packet find their way internally to the appropriate area where the eggs are fertilized. In some leeches, the spermat-

These reproductive worms develop either by transform... of the non-reproductive kind, or by bud formatio... reproductive worm from the hind end or sides of... reproductive animal. In some species the reproductiv... iduals break off from the male or female worm from... they developed.

...en the reproductive male and female worms migrate... e numbers to the surface of the sea and begin to shed ...perm and eggs, this is called swarming. There is ... e that some females secrete a substance which at- ...e males, and that the shedding of sperm by the ...ts as a stimulant for the females to shed eggs. The ...fertilized in the seawater.

... the fascinating aspects of swarming is that it is ...her rigid control in some species. Although no ...or seems to be involved, it is seasonal; light, ...wave action, hormones secreted by the brain, all

with modified tail segments heavily laden

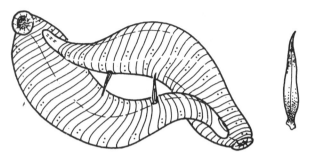

Figure 47.

Reciprocal copulation between two leeches in which the packages of sperm (spermatophores) are driven through the skin of each partner. An enlarged spermatophore on the right.

...ophore simply sticks into another leech and acts as a bridge for the reciprocal transfer of sperm.

Each hermaphroditic leech, having received sperm from its mate, proceeds to fertilize its eggs internally and lays these eggs into a cocoon which slips over the head end. The glandular collar of the leech secretes both the cocoon and nutrients for the development of the young.

Although the cocoons are laid free or are attached to objects on land or in water, sometimes they are affixed to the body of the leech and are carried until the young hatch out.

Sexual Metamorphosis

Polychaetes are a diverse and abundant group of marine annelid worms that live mostly on the sea floor off coastal areas. Although most are free-moving, some are sedentary tube-dwellers. They are extremely important in the food chain of the sea. Some polychaetes reproduce asexually by the budding process, where the body divides into several pieces that develop into new worms. Most members of the group, however, undergo sexual reproduction, and there are some examples of fascinating and bizarre activities during the process.

The females of a certain species of polychaete are cannibalistic in that they bite off and swallow the hind end of the male worm, that part which contains sperm. After the sperm are swallowed by the female, they penetrate her intestine and fertilize eggs within the body cavity. Her body then ruptures, and the fertilized eggs are set free to develop in the seawater. Both male and female worms regenerate the lost parts of their bodies. If sperm and eggs are taken from these worms and maintained in seawater under laboratory conditions, fertilization does not occur. The conclusion is that some substance in the female intestine is necessary for fertilization of the eggs.

There are no permanent ovaries and testes in polychaete worms. The eggs of the female and sperm of the male develop from the lining of the body cavity. Since the animal has no ducts, secondary sexual structures, or genital pores, these gametes (once matured in the fluid of the body cavity) either erupt through the body wall of the parent worm which then dies, or, in other species, the eggs or sperm are conducted out by the tubes of the kidney.

Some remarkable phenomena occur in the formation of reproductive individuals and their later swarming activities to the ocean surface. At certain times of the year, individual non-reproductive males and females will change

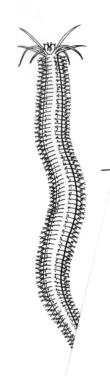
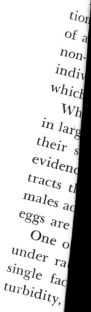

tion
of a
non-
indiv
which
Wh
in larg
their s
evidenc
tracts t
males ac
eggs are
One o
under ra
single fac
turbidity,

Figure 48.

Body transfor
A normal wo
(right) packe

(either p
There a
of the e
and sp

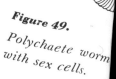

Figure 49.

Polychaete worm
with sex cells.

influence the activity to some degree. Of special interest is the fact that in some species swarming has been shown to occur with rather precise lunar periodicity. The palolo worm, which lives off the coast of Samoa and Fiji, regularly swarms at dawn on the first day of the last quarter of the October–November moon. The density of the writhing worms is so great that the surface of the sea becomes milky. The people of the area prize the worms as food, either raw or baked. Birds and fish also have a feast once a year on the palolo worm.

Just as a lobster would molt continuously were it not for inhibitory substances released from the brain, there are substances secreted by some polychaete worms which inhibit the formation of reproductive individuals. If the brain of a polychaete is removed, production of a reproductive worm follows immediately. If the brain of a young worm is grafted into an adult, the formation of reproductive individuals is suppressed.

Parasitic Sex

A small group of sausage-shaped worms called echiurids dwell on the sea bottom in burrows, tubes, and shells of other animals. They are found not only in coastal waters of warm seas, but also in great depths of the North Pacific. Attached to the cylindrical body is a prominent proboscis, which is really the head of the animal since it contains the brain. The mouth is located at the junction of the proboscis and trunk, and the animal eats debris which is trapped on mucus secreted by the snout and directed toward the oral opening by way of folds or a gutter along the proboscis. The worms keep their bodies secluded and expose only the proboscis (which is very contractile) for feeding purposes.

Echiurids are either male or female. The single testis or ovary develops from the body cavity lining and the eggs or sperm mature in the body cavity fluid. Since there are no sexual ducts, the kidney ducts serve as an outlet for the eggs and sperm. The free-swimming larvae develop into adult worms.

Species of the echiurid, such as *Bonnelia*, exhibit some of the most bizarre manners of sexual reproduction. Although the female worm is about three feet long, the male measures a fraction of an inch. The female has a complete echiurid body, but the male lacks a proboscis, mouth, and anus. Not only does the male exhibit extreme sexual dimorphism, but he lives most of his life as a parasite inside the kidney of the female worm.

The female *Bonnelia*'s eggs are fertilized inside her single kidney by her parasitic mate, and the fertilized eggs are then passed into the seawater by way of the kidney

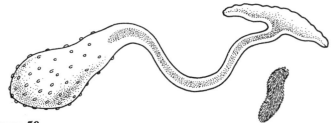

Figure 50.

A female echiurid worm on the left and a pygmy male on the right (greatly enlarged). The highly modified male lives in the kidney of the female and fertilizes her eggs there.

opening. There is evidence that the female secretes a substance affecting the sexual development of the free-swimming larvae, which have the potential of being either male or female. Any larva developing on the bottom isolated from the female worm will always become a female. Larvae which develop on or very near the female are retarded in their development and become males. These tiny males may reside for a time on the surface of the female worm, or in her mouth, but their eventual destiny is her kidney.

A third kind of development occurs when larvae settle on the female worm for some time and then are removed for various reasons. In such cases the larvae develop features of both sexes, having functional male testes, but also such female features as a proboscis.

Sex by the Arm

Cephalopods are a group of marine mollusks which include the squid and the octopus. Squid have a head, neck, slender cylindrical trunk, and ten pairs of arms that attach to the head end. One pair of arms is longer and these are called tentacles. All arms have suction cups on the inner surface for capturing prey—mostly fish. The squid is able to swim quickly backward or forward by means of a funnel-shaped siphon which functions on the jet propulsion principle. The octopus is closely related to the squid, but has a globular body and eight arms attached to the head. Squid are usually found in packs in open water, whereas octopuses most often live alone on the ocean bottom.

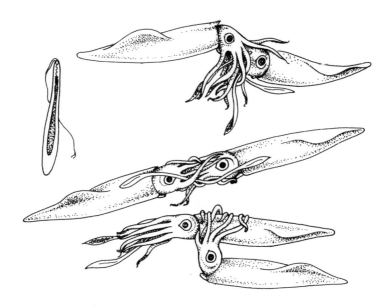

Figure 51.

Copulating squid in various positions. Top pair is in a pre-copulatory embrace. In the middle pair, the male (on the right) is grasping a spermatophore released from his siphon. In the lower pair, the male (on the bottom) is placing a package of sperm inside the body cavity of the female. Inset shows an enlarged spermatophore.

Both the squid and the octopus accomplish sexual reproduction in a very unusual manner. The animals are male or female, having either a single large ovary or testis. From these gonads a duct connected with a series of gland structures leads toward the siphon, ending as an opening on the siphon wall. In the female these glands add yolk,

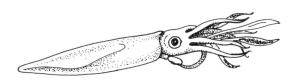

Figure 52.

The arm of a female squid grasping an egg coming out of her siphon.

gelatinous mass, and membranes to the egg. In the male, the sperm cells are bundled as packets (spermatophores), each one having an ejaculatory apparatus with a cap that can trigger the packet off.

The male and female squid undergo courtship, lining up head-to-head with the arms of each animal embracing the other. As the packet of sperm emerges from the siphon of the male, he reaches down with either the left or right fourth arm, grasps the sperm packet, and, in some species, places it in a pocket just under the mouth of the female. The female then releases her egg masses, which are held in her arms. The sperm packets are triggered off, and fertilization of the eggs occurs while she is holding the eggs in her arms in front of her head. In other species the fourth arm of the male plucks the sperm packet from his siphon and places it inside the body of the female, through open spaces between the neck and trunk of the animal. In this species, eggs are fertilized internally.

The male octopus strokes the female with his tentacles to put her in a responsive mood. Then, with his third arm he

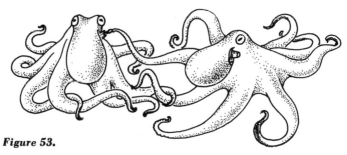

Figure 53.

Copulation by the arm. The male octopus (on the right) uses his arm to place a package of sperm through the siphon and inside the body of the female.

grasps his sperm packet from the siphon opening and places it inside the body of the female. When he does this, the tip of the arm detaches and remains viable inside the female along with the sperm packet.

The copulatory arm of cephalopods (which functions as a penis) varies according to the species. In some species, the small suckers on the arm are lined up to form a groove along the entire length, serving as a conduit for sperm packets; in others, there is either a depression or an actual cavity in the arm where the sperm packets are collected.

The female squid attaches her egg masses in strings to the ocean bottom—commonly called "dead man's fingers" —and then goes off and leaves them. The female octopus fastens the eggs to rocks and other hard substances and then stands guard over them for several weeks, caring for them by hosing the eggs off with a jet stream from her siphon. This serves to keep the eggs free of debris and infection from microorganisms.

The Dominant Female Rotifer

Rotifers are among the oddest creatures known. Most of them are freshwater inhabitants, although some species live in the sea and among damp mosses on land. They are mostly microscopic in size, some having the remarkable ability to lose water from their bodies, dry up completely, and remain dormant for many years. When water is again available, they take it in and become active within a very short period of time. In their dormant state, some species can withstand subfreezing temperatures for long periods of time.

All rotifers have a head, trunk, and a footlike hind end. The head has an active wheellike apparatus covered with cilia. The animals also have strong jaws with teeth in the first part of the intestinal tract. This structure can be everted through the mouth. Their reproductive activities are as unusual as their biological features.

Freshwater rotifers are mostly females, the males being very uncommon. In some species, there are no males at all, and the females lay eggs which simply develop into other females. In other species, the males are always present, and the female lays fertilized eggs. Half the offspring are males and the other half females, and the females of this type of rotifer cannot reproduce parthenogenetically.

Rotifers living in temporary bodies of water have rather complicated reproductive activities. In early spring the rotifers are all females, laying unfertilized eggs which always develop into other females. Then later in the season these parthenogenetic females begin laying eggs which can be fertilized. If these eggs are not fertilized, they develop into males; if they are fertilized, the eggs acquire a thicker

resistant shell. These so-called resting or winter eggs remain
dormant, withstand drying and freezing, and can be blown
about by the wind, or be carried on bodies of other animals.
In the spring, the fertilized winter eggs hatch into female
rotifers, and this pattern of reproduction begins all over
again.

Female rotifers have a single ovary and a tube which
leads the eggs to the cloaca, a pouch at the hind end of the
animal which expels both feces and eggs. Some rotifers
have yolk glands associated with the female reproductive
system.

Male rotifers (when they exist) are about one-fourth the
size of the female and have a single testis with a sperm duct
leading to a pore at the rear end. Some male rotifers have
an eversible penis. Fertilization occurs mostly by the hypodermic impregnation method, where sperm enter the female through the body wall and eventually reach her body
cavity where fertilization occurs.

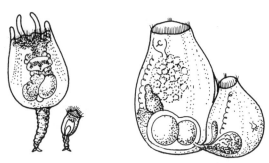

Figure 54.

*Sexual dimorphism and copulation in rotifers: (left figure)—
large female and small male; (right figure)—small male copulating with larger female.*

Some male rotifers release their sperm in packets, although this is not common. The sperm are of two types, one for fertilizing eggs, and the other to aid the penetration of the sperm through the body wall of the female. Even though the male rotifer lives only a few days, lacks a mouth, and does not feed, it has the important role of fertilizing eggs that can survive winter months.

Sex Reversal: The Snail

Gastropods are a large, diverse group of mollusks which inhabit the ocean, fresh water, and land. They include pond and garden snails, slugs, and the diverse snails at the edge of the sea. Some snails are either male or female, but more than half are hermaphroditic, having a single gonad (the ovotestis) which produces both eggs and sperm. However, the rest of the reproductive systems in a given hermaphroditic snail are separated anatomically or functionally, so that self-fertilization does not occur. The snail *Crepidula* (commonly called slipper shells or boat shells) exhibits sex reversal from male to female.

Crepidula snails are gregarious and mostly attached, either to each other in stacks, or on the shells of such things as oysters and scallops. When a stack of snails is examined, it is found not only that the smallest ones on top are males and the largest ones on the bottom are females, but that the snails in the middle of the stack are in the process of changing from males to females.

Studies of this fascinating animal have shown the following: if males are removed from the stack and isolated from females, they will become females; if males are re-

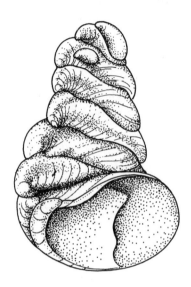

Figure 55.

Sex switching in snails. A stack of snails in which the large animals on the bottom are females, the small ones on top are males, and those in the middle are males changing to females.

moved from the stack but kept in the same aquarium with females, physically isolated from them by a screen, they will remain males; males will always remain males if they are attached to females; once a snail is a female, it always remains a female; if the larvae settle close to female snails, the larvae always become males; if they settle away from females, they become females.

As in species of echiurid, it appears that the female snails emit substances into the water which govern the sexual development of the males, and that determination of the sex of these animals is far from rigid.

The Dart-Throwing Helix

In France, the land snail *Helix* is cultivated in snail gardens and eaten by the hundreds of millions annually. This hermaphroditic snail has a single gonad producing both sperm and eggs, but the male and female reproductive systems are separated internally. Each empties into a genital pocket which opens by a pore on the right side of the head. On one side of the genital pocket is a penis, and on the other side is a vagina.

Even though the snails are hermaphroditic, they reproduce by cross-fertilization, and it is accomplished in a curious manner. Two snails prepared to mate approach each other with their genital pockets pushed out of the genital pores on their heads. When they are close enough, each snail shoots a dart from the genital pore; the darts penetrate deeply into the body of each partner. The darts

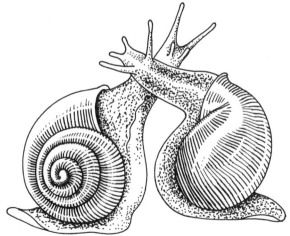

Figure 56.

Reciprocal copulation between two hermaphroditic snails.

are formed in a little sac which empties into the genital pocket and they serve to stimulate copulation.

After each animal receives its dart, the snails copulate, each inserting its penis into the vagina of the other. The sperm are mutually transferred as packets and are stored in a blind pouch which joins the vagina. The snails then separate and later lay fertilized eggs that eventually hatch into baby snails.

Making Use of the Mouth and Intestine

Ctenophores (commonly called sea gooseberries, sea walnuts, or comb jellies) are a group of small marine animals which at certain times of the year are very dense in surface waters. Most of them are an inch or two in diameter and usually have two very long tentacles trailing from a transparent body. The tentacles are used to capture prey, such as small fish, plankton, and various fish eggs, which is then brought to the mouth located at one end of the animal. Ctenophores are capable of emitting spectacular luminescence at the ocean surface.

Ctenophores are all hermaphroditic and have male and female gonads along the branches of the intestine, but most are without ducts, tubes, or reproductive pores for the passage of sperm or eggs. The animal has overcome this obstacle by making use of its mouth and intestine.

The ctenophore does not self-fertilize. Instead, the mature eggs and sperm are released into the intestinal branches and then shed directly into the water through the mouth opening. The eggs are fertilized in the seawater where they develop into free-swimming larvae.

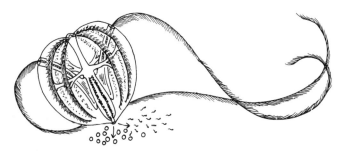

Figure 57.

Animals such as ctenophores release eggs and sperm through the mouth opening.

More Sex Reversal: Clams and Oysters

Sexually-reproducing animals are usually considered to be either male or female. Invertebrates demonstrate indifference to this rigid distinction, however, and none more than certain clams and oysters.

Most bivalved mollusks are either male or female and release sperm and eggs into the water through their reproductive or kidney ducts. (Some species have a single gonad that releases eggs and sperm from different portions of that organ.) Fertilization and development usually take place in water, although there are species in which fertilization and development occur internally, and baby clams are born fully developed.

For some clams and oysters, however, sex switching is part of the normal life cycle. The quahog of the Atlantic Coast (which is used in clam chowder, or when still young, eaten as cherrystone clams) is first male and then female,

Figure 58.

Many mollusks (such as the quahog on the left and the oyster on the right) routinely change their sex from male to female.

which it stays for the rest of its life; a small percentage of quahogs remain either male or female. Some clams and oysters go one step further, changing from males to females and, after spawning, reversing back to males again. The sex changes of some bivalves are induced by environmental factors such as available food supply and water temperature, but in all cases, a small constant proportion of animals remains male or female.

Courtship Maneuvers of the Spider

The sexual act is potentially dangerous to some male animals. The female spider for instance seems more interested in eating than mating, and often her first meal after copulation is the male himself.

There are a number of ways in which the male spider attracts the attention of females, but most are designed to help him determine whether he will live to mate again

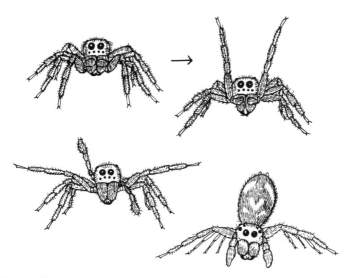

Figure 59.

Courtship behavior in some male spiders: (top figures)—
moving front legs up and down; (lower left figure)—alternate
lifting of palps; (lower right figure)—legs spread out and tail
high in the air.

another day. Some engage in a variety of courtship move-
ments and dances. Some pluck the spider web and produce
vibrations which the females recognize as mating calls.
The male of a certain species pounces on the female, strokes
her, and even pounds on her, apparently to subdue his
potential partner before mating.

In some species, the male guards against being eaten by
locking his fangs with those of the female. When he is
finished mating, he lowers a silk line and scampers away.
Some males are very cautious and will mate with a partner

only after tying her down with a length of silk. Other males offer their potential mate a meal of an insect wrapped in silk. Some females, however, are also adept at tying up their partners. These hapless males mate only once and are then eaten.

Whatever the courtship behavior, during actual mating male spiders use their front claws to transmit sperm to their female partners. The male discharges sperm from his genital opening and scoops it into a reservoir in his front claws. The male's blood pressure goes up, and the claws swell with blood and become erectile. This triggers the release of sperm from the male's claw, which is inserted into the genital opening of the female.

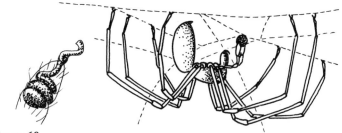

Figure 60.

Male spider charging his palp appendage with a glob of sperm he has discharged on a web. An enlargement of the palp is on the left.

The Captive Male Barnacle

Barnacles are marine animals that live in large colonies and attach themselves to a variety of underwater objects, including other barnacles. They are hermaphroditic but

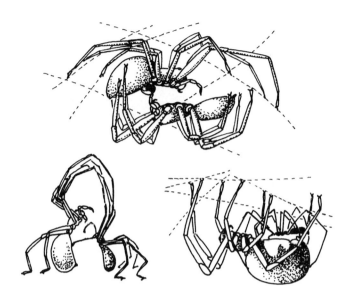

Figure 61.

Various positions in mating spiders. By means of their palps charged with sperm, the males are inserting sperm into the genital openings of the females.

reproduce by cross-fertilization. One animal deposits sperm near the female opening of another. Eggs are fertilized internally and are then brooded until the larvae hatch. The larvae live freely at this early stage of their development.

In some species of barnacle, the male is a captive within the female, or even within a hermaphroditic animal. Such males are dwarfed, do not have a free-living existence, and spend their lives within other barnacles.

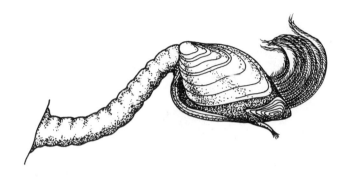

Figure 62.

Attached hermaphroditic barnacle; extruded penis (lower right).

Barnacles that bore into and live inside the shells of other animals have separate sexes, with extreme size difference between the males and females. The males consist of little more than a sac containing reproductive structures, among which is a proportionately large penis. The females carry around a dozen or more such males.

Reproductive Curiosities

There are a variety of behavioral and functional aspects of sexual reproduction in non-backboned animals that are best listed as statements of interest.

There is courtship behavior in many invertebrates—dancing in crabs and scorpions, wrestling in squids, and clawing in spiders.

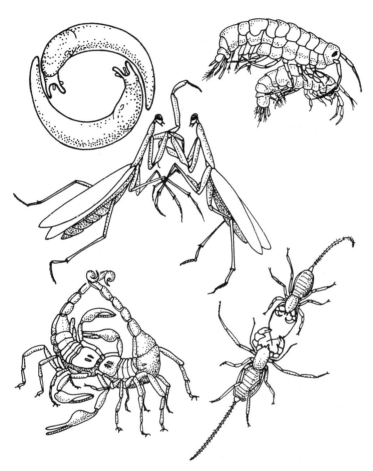

Figure 63.

Courtship behavior in some invertebrates: (top figures)—slugs licking each other, and male amphipod in precopulatory position above a female; (center figure)—praying mantises in a dance; (lower figures)—prenuptial dance of scorpions, and male whip scorpion grasping front legs of female.

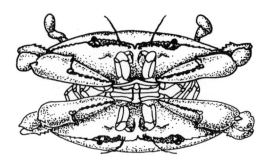

Figure 64.

Male and female crabs copulating, male above female.

Most male crabs copulate from above the female, who lies on her back. However, some place themselves at right angles to the female. Male crayfish and lobsters turn the female on her back and copulate with her from above.

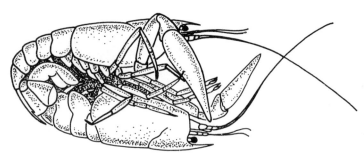

Figure 65.

Male crayfish copulating with a female lying on her back. Although the male has no penis, he transfers sperm from openings on the bottom side of his abdomen to openings on the abdomen of the female by means of modified appendages.

Some male ostracods (mussel shrimps) have a double penis and the females have a double genital opening.

The male horseshoe crab mounts the female from the rear. He then discharges sperm into a sand depression which the female has scooped out beneath her. She lays her eggs into this depression while mating and then covers the fertilized eggs.

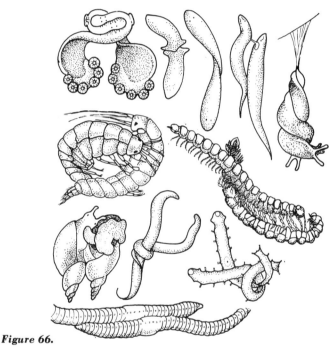

Figure 66.

Various styles of copulation: (first row)—side-to-side, head-to-head, tail-to-tail, and hypodermic impregnation in flatworms; copulating slugs suspended from an attached mucous strand; (second row)—male amphipod and millipede above females; (third row)—snails, nematodes, and gastrotrichs in side position; (bottom figure)—reciprocal copulation in annelids.

In some jellyfish, the sperm enter through the female's mouth, fertilization is internal, and fertilized eggs or larvae are released through her mouth.

Some snails engage in group sex; several animals form a line or a circle and all copulate with a partner—except for those at the end of the line.

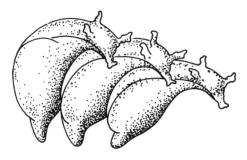

Figure 67.

Group sex in three hermaphroditic snails. The animal on the left has a penis in the middle snail, which has a penis in the snail on the right.

Freshwater clams release shelled larvae which must attach to and nourish on fish before they can develop into adults.

Some sea cucumbers brood their young inside their bodies, and at birth the entire end of the animal ruptures and then regenerates after releasing the young.

Some starfish brood eggs in pockets just under the skin.

Some female sea slugs lay a half billion eggs in a season.

Even though earthworms stick together and mate for several hours, fertilization of eggs takes place much later, outside of each hermaphroditic worm.

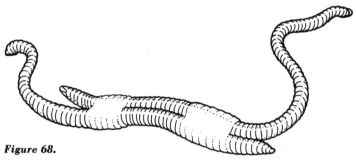

Figure 68.

Earthworms mating. Although these hermaphroditic animals do not have a penis, they stick together and mutually exchange sperm. Eggs are fertilized later in each separate animal.

A fluke parasitic on the gills of fish exists in pairs, the body of each worm fused with its mate in permanent copulation.

In some polychaetes, the male wraps his body around the female so that his anus is over her mouth. He releases his sperm which fertilizes the eggs inside her body cavity. She later lays the eggs out her anus.

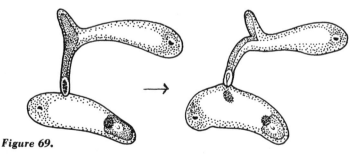

Figure 69.

Hypodermic impregnation in a flatworm; sperm are injected through the skin of the partner.

In some turbellarians, there are two reproductive openings, one for receiving sperm during copulation, and the other for releasing fertilized eggs.

In flagellates that live inside the intestine of termites, molting hormones of the termite stimulate the sexual activity of the protozoans.

Insects usually mate only once and quite quickly, but some (such as dragonflies) fly around in an embrace for hours and even days.

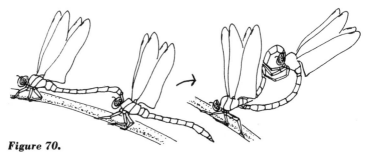

Figure 70.

Copulation in dragonflies. In figure on left, the male grasps the head of the female with his tail claspers; the female then swings her genital opening (near her tail) under the body of the male and receives sperm from his genital opening, located in the front part of his body.

Male silkworm moths are attracted from miles away by specific odors released by females of the same species. If juice is squeezed out of the female and placed near the male, he will attempt to copulate with the juice.

The chirps of many insects are the sounds of courtship. Many female mosquitoes vibrate their wings, attracting males by the sound. If a tuning fork is vibrated at a certain

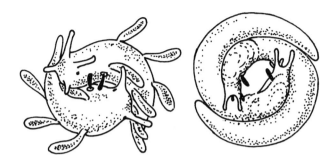

Figure 71.

Reciprocal copulation in two species of hermaphroditic slugs.

frequency, male mosquitoes will fly toward the tuning fork and attempt to mate with females in the area.

The time interval between flashes emitted by male fireflies is the signal that attracts the females to mate.

The female cricket courts the male and then mounts him.

The male millipede runs up the back of the female to test if she has already mated. If she has not, she will not move, and the male crawls under her and copulates. If she inches off, the male knows she has fertilized eggs inside her and he does not pursue her.

The penis, when it is present in non-backboned animals, has a variety of shapes and sizes.

The penis of insects is usually pointed backward inside the body and is everted for copulation. Because of this, and because the penis usually has certain irregularities on it, there are many unusual mating positions, even a tail-to-tail position. The penis of the male honeybee breaks off after mating with the queen bee, and he then bleeds to death.

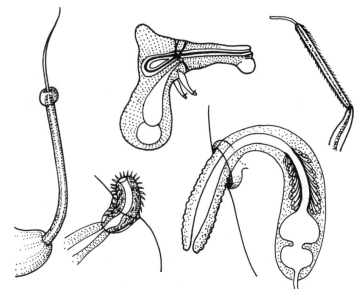

Figure 72.

Penises of some invertebrates. Starting with figure on left, moving clockwise—long nematode penis with knob and spine at tip, dwarf male barnacle with enormous club-shaped penis, nematode penis with spine at tip, fluke penis with warts, and fluke penis with spines.

Figure 73.

Male flea with a coiled penis.

The female praying mantis eats the head of her mate while he is copulating from above her.

Some female millipedes will vomit or defecate, shape the material into a cup, lay a single egg into it, close it, and polish it. When the young millipede hatches, the dried vomitus or dung becomes its first meal.

Both male and female dung beetles cooperate in rolling up balls of feces in which the eggs develop.

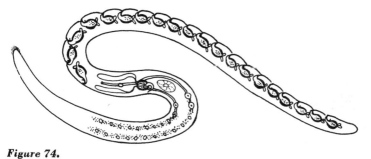

Figure 74.

A flatworm with twenty extra penises. Only one is used for reproductive purposes.

6 Alternation and Combination of Methods

EVERY animal is a combination of its genetic endowment and environmental adaptation. All life begins as a single cell, and this basic unit of life has the machinery to self-duplicate; cells are essentially copying machines. As has been shown, invertebrate animals can reproduce themselves asexually, sexually, or most interesting of all, by combining both methods. The various styles of asexual reproduction are highly efficient, producing, in a relatively short period of time, a large number of offspring that are exact genetic copies of the parent that produced them.

The offspring of sexually-reproducing animals resemble the parents in form and size but they are not genetic copies. The essential advantage of sexual reproduction is that it provides for great genetic variability in the offspring. Although their reproductive rate is lower than that of asexual animals, sexual reproducers have the potential to survive and multiply in harmony with the slow but steady changes that are always occurring in the environment.

Alternations of both methods combine the high efficiency of uniparental fission (in terms of numbers of offspring) and the benefits of genetic variability associated with sex. Many animal groups use a combination of reproductive methods to produce offspring, but nowhere is there such a spectrum of reproductive variation as among colonial flagellated protozoans (which are mostly plantlike organisms). *Gonium* is a colony made up of four cells, all of equal size. Each cell is capable of dividing asexually twice, so that four new colonies of four cells each can develop from the original parent colony. The colony can also reproduce sexually, in that any of the four cells can break away from the parent colony and fuse with other similar-sized cells to produce a zygote. The zygote then divides twice to produce a colony of four cells.

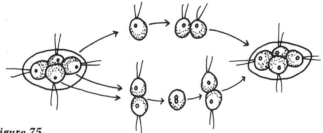

Figure 75.

Gonium, *a flagellated protozoan colony. New colonies may form by asexual fission of any cell (top route), or sexually by cells acting as gametes (bottom route).*

A *Pandorina* colony is constructed of sixteen equal-size cells in a solid mass. Each of these cells is capable of dividing four times to produce a new colony of sixteen cells. Or, each of the sixteen cells can reproduce sexually, but in this case the cells develop into either small (male) or large

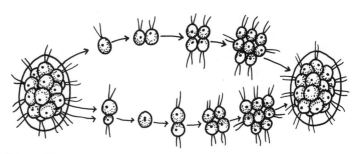

Figure 76.

A Pandorina *colony. Reproduction may occur by asexual fission of any cell (top route), or by zygote formation (bottom route). In this flagellated protozoan, the sex cells are of unequal size.*

(female) gametes. After fertilization, the zygote divides four times to produce a new colony of sixteen cells.

A *Eudorina* colony is a hollow ball of thirty-two cells, all of the same size. It reproduces both asexually and sexually as *Pandorina*, except that the cells of the parent colony are twice those of *Pandorina*.

It is in *Pleodorina* that there is a division of labor in the thirty-two cells that make up the colony. One end of the colony is composed of twenty-eight similar cells that can reproduce asexually into new colonies, but the opposite end has four smaller cells which never divide. The large cells also have the capacity to form gametes of unequal size and the zygotes of such fertilization eventually produce colonies similar to the original parent.

The zenith of sexual reproduction in colonial flagellates occurs in *Volvox*, colonies of which may be composed of

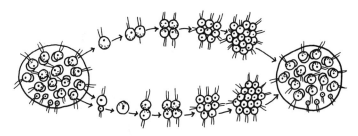

Figure 77.

In Pleodorina, *four small cells of the thirty-two making up the protozoan colony are unable to reproduce either asexually or sexually. The other twenty-eight cells may produce new colonies either by asexual fission (top route) or sexually with gametes of unequal size (bottom route).*

20,000 cells. Not only are some cells always reproductive and others non-reproductive, and not only do new colonies develop and eventually break out of the original colony, but distinct eggs, sperm, and zygotes are formed inside the

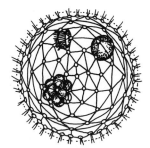

Figure 78.

A Volvox *colony constructed of many cells. A new colony is developing by asexual fission (lower left), and a packet of sperm (upper left) and an ovum (upper right) will contribute to sexual reproduction within the colony.*

parent. The latter eventually divide asexually to the number of cells characteristic for the species. Although most colonies are hermaphroditic, developing both eggs and sperm, some species have unisexuality in that they always produce either male or female gametes.

Foraminiferans are shelled amoebae, mostly of the sea. The organisms live in either single- or multi-chambered shells that are perforated with many openings through which fine pseudopodia extend. In any given species there are two types of individuals, and the life cycle of these

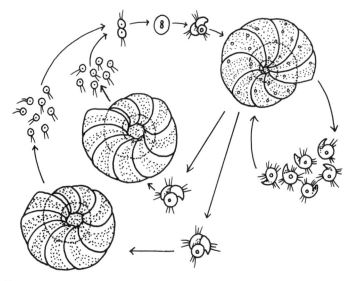

Figure 79.

Alternation of asexual and sexual reproduction in foraminiferans. The protozoan in the upper right routinely produces offspring by asexual fission, but at certain periods some of the progeny will develop into foraminiferans which emit sex cells resulting in zygote formation (lower and upper left).

organisms routinely involves an alternation of asexual and sexual modes of reproduction. One type of individual undergoes multiple fission and produces many offspring similar to itself. At certain periods, however, some of these offspring develop into foraminiferans which eventually will produce numbers of flagellated gametes, or sex cells. Fertilization occurs to produce zygotes, which then develop into asexual organisms.

The sporozoans are a group of unicellular organisms which are all intracellular parasites of other animals—both invertebrates and vertebrates. They usually have very complicated life cycles (involving mostly two hosts), exhibiting both sexual reproduction by gametes and various modifications of multiple fission. Only two types of the parasite will be considered.

Gregarines are parasites of invertebrates. Two entire organisms fuse with each other, form a cyst around them-

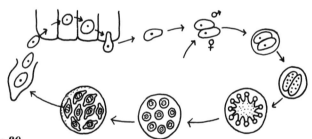

Figure 80.

Combination of sexual and asexual reproduction in a gregarine. The sporozoan matures in the host cells (upper left), and then each protozoan produces many gametes of equal size (right center). Each zygote produces many spores by asexual fission (lower left).

selves, and then produce many gametes within the cyst. Fertilization takes place within the cyst, and each zygote then produces many offspring (spores) by a series of multiple fissions. The offspring then become active parasites within the cells of the host, and eventually complete the cycle by producing gametes as did their parents.

Coccidia are intracellular parasites of both vertebrates and invertebrates and have a cycle in which the vegetative organisms routinely undergo multiple fission inside the cells they parasitize. These progeny keep reinfecting other cells and also undergo multiple fission, but every few generations they produce gametes or sex cells. The sex cells are very unequal in size and form and are therefore called male and female gametes. The gametes produce zygotes, which in turn produce spores by the process of multiple fission. These spores must be eaten by a host, and the offspring begin the cycle all over again. Malaria is a kind of coccidial infection of blood cells. One of the dif-

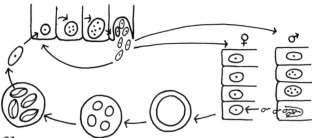

Figure 81.

Alternation of asexual and sexual reproduction in a coccidian. The parasite routinely reproduces by multiple fission in host tissue (upper left). At certain periods gamete formation also occurs (on the right), followed by asexual formation of spores (lower left).

ferences in the life cycle of this parasite (which reproduces both sexually and asexually) is that the offspring are injected into a host by a mosquito, in which part of the life cycle of the parasite has developed.

Sponges reproduce in a number of ways. The key to all of them is the multipotential cell which has the capacity to develop into other cell types of the sponge body. Colonies of sponges are formed by external buds which remain attached to the parent. Sponges have remarkable powers of regeneration, and any piece constricted or broken off develops into a new colony. Freshwater sponges, and a few marine species, form internal buds or gemmules. These have a tough cover around them and are highly resistant to drying and low temperatures. When the parent sponge distintegrates, the gemmules are released, and when water conditions are favorable, the cells inside the gemmule emerge and develop into new offspring.

Sponges also reproduce sexually, producing both eggs and sperm inside their bodies. Most are hermaphroditic although some colonies are always either male or female. The hermaphroditic species produce male and female gametes at different times so that they actually function as separate sexes. The eggs remain in the sponge, but the sperm are released and enter other sponges by way of the current of water which is always passing through their bodies. Fertilization and partial development occurs within the sponge, but larvae are released and have a free-living existence before they settle down and develop.

Most coelenterates are marine and polymorphic (having different kinds of bodies at different times) and usually have complex life cycles. All have various forms of asexual budding and/or fission as well as sexual means of reproduc-

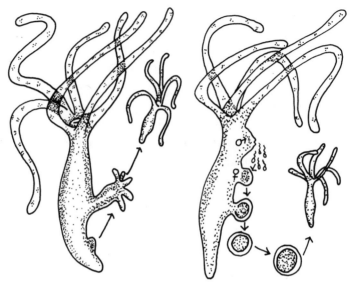

Figure 82.

In the coelenterate Hydra, *asexual reproduction may occur by budding (left figure), or sexually by gamete formation (right figure).*

tion. *Hydra* is a fresh water coelenterate, essentially a hollow tube closed at one end, with a mouth and tentacles at the other. During the warmer periods of the year, it reproduces asexually by forming buds from the body wall. These buds develop into complete young offspring before they detach from the parent and go off on their own. They usually bud off one at a time, but sometimes there are several from a single parent. As might be expected, they also have great capabilities of regeneration.

These animals also engage in sexual reproduction in the

fall. They have a multipotential cell and gametes or sex cells develop from accumulations of these cells. Large eggs develop and protrude from the basal portion of the body, and testes grow as bumps on the upper body portions. The testes have nipples with openings through which sperm are released, and the egg is fertilized in place. The zygote then undergoes partial development, encloses itself with a shell-like material, and then drops off the parent. It remains in this protective state until spring when further development takes place, and a young hydra eventually hatches out of the case.

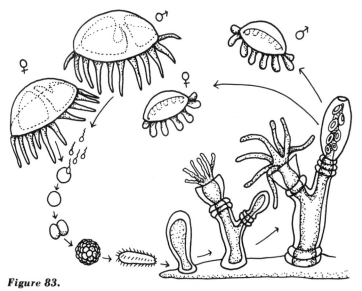

Figure 83.

Asexual and sexual reproduction in the coelenterate Obelia. *Certain individuals in the colony (lower right) bud male and female jellyfish, which then swim off. The free-living jellyfish release eggs and sperm, and each larva attaches and forms a new colony by budding.*

Obelia is a colonial marine coelenterate comprised of two types of individuals. One type (the hydranth) deals with feeding activities, and the other (the gonangium) with reproduction. All of the individuals in the colony are formed by budding from an original hydroid that attaches to a substrate, such as wharves and pilings. It is the reproductive individual that is the link in the rest of the life cycle of this organism. The gonangium buds offspring which are released from the colony and develop into bell-shaped, free-living forms called medusae. These are either male or female and develop internal gonads. Sperm and eggs are released into the water by these sexual individuals,

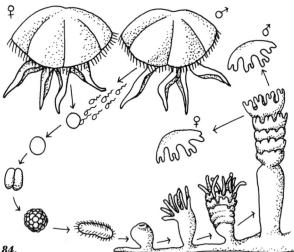

Figure 84.

Sexual and asexual reproduction in the coelenterate Aurelia.
Male and female jellyfish (upper left) release gametes, and the formed larva attaches and develops into an individual that buds off progeny by asexual fission (lower right).

and after fertilization of the eggs, a free-swimming ciliated larva develops. Eventually the larva will settle down and, by means of extensive budding, create a new colony having both feeding and reproductive individuals.

Aurelia is a coelenterate that belongs to a group commonly referred to as jellyfish. The medusae of this organism are either male or female, are free-living, and release eggs and sperm into the seawater. Fertilization of eggs and development of larvae are similar to that described for *Obelia*. It differs from *Obelia* in that when its larva settles down, it produces not a colony but a single individual. This individual has the form of a feeding type at first, but then begins to develop many disklike buds from its free end. These buds develop into male and female medusae to complete the life cycle.

The group of flatworms to which planarians belong can reproduce either asexually or sexually. The worm can constrict across its body. The pieces then separate and regenerate the missing parts, keeping the polarity of the

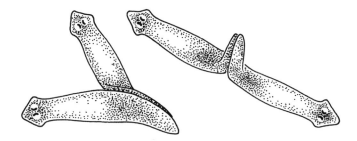

Figure 85.

Reciprocal copulation in planaria. The penis of each hermaphroditic animal transfers sperm into the genital opening of its partner.

original parent. Obviously, this kind of animal has out-standing capabilities of regeneration. Even though planar-ians are hermaphroditic, an individual does not fertilize itself. What happens in sexual reproduction is that two worms place their hind ends together (either facing away from each other or in the same direction), and the penis of each animal is inserted into the genital opening of the other. Sperm is mutually transferred, and the worms then separate after mating. The eggs are fertilized, yolk is added, and the zygotes are enclosed in a capsule before being re-leased from each worm. Young planaria hatch out after some weeks of development inside the cocoon.

Trematodes or flukes are another kind of flatworm, in which the animals are almost always hermaphroditic; in fact most of the structure of these animals is made up of female and male reproductive systems. In the life cycle of most species, the adult worms live inside all types of vertebrates, and the larval stages develop inside a mollusk (usually a snail). As in planarians, the flukes usually under-go cross-fertilization in which sperm from one worm is transferred to the genital opening of another during mating. However, these animals function either as males or females. The adult worm then lays fertilized eggs which pass out of the host in which the parasite lives. These eggs either hatch and penetrate a snail, or are eaten by it. It is within the snail that there are many generations of larval forms that develop from an original zygote, and these develop by larvae producing more larvae. The progeny that develop from a single egg may number in the thousands. The life cycle is completed when the last larval stage produced in the snail is released and gets back into

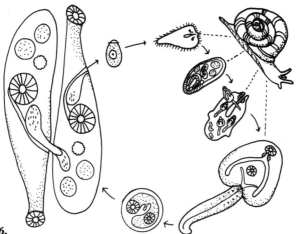

Figure 86.

Sexual and asexual reproduction in a fluke. In the pair of worms on the left, one is depositing sperm into a receptacle of its partner. A larva develops inside each egg released from the fertilized worm and gains entrance into a snail. Within the mollusk several generations and thousands of larvae develop from a single egg by asexual polyembryony (upper right).

the original host by a variety of methods, depending on the species of fluke. The production of enormous numbers of larvae compensates for the hazards of the complicated life cycles of these worms.

Tapeworms may be thought of as a series of reproductive units attached to a head-and-neck region. These units are constructed of both well-developed male and female reproductive systems. The tapeworm buds off new units from the neck region. In most tapeworms, the series of units behind the head are not fully developed. This is followed

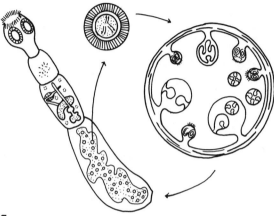

Figure 87.

Although tapeworms add on segments by asexual budding, they also reproduce sexually, by themselves or with partners. In some species, a single fertilized egg (upper center), when swallowed by another host, can produce many incipient tapeworms by asexual budding (figure on right). Each one has the potential to develop into an adult worm when eaten by a proper host.

by a series of units that are fully matured, and the tail end of the worm has a series in which most structures have deteriorated except for the uterus heavily laden with thousands of eggs. These animals are probably the most sexually versatile of all creatures, because a mature unit can fertilize itself or mate with other units of the worm, or with units of a different worm.

In addition to the asexual budding occurring continu-

ously in the adult tapeworm, in many species asexual budding takes place in a variety of larval worms that are part of
some complicated life cycles involving hosts other than the
one in which the adult tapeworm lives. An extreme example of this is in the larval form of *Echinococcus*, in which
thousands of tapeworm heads develop from an original
zygote produced by sexual fertilization.

The nemertine ribbon worms are mostly marine animals
that range in length from an inch to several feet. The sexes
are usually separate, and each sex has paired multiple
gonads, discharging their eggs and sperm through ducts
into the water. Eggs are fertilized there and eventually
develop into new worms. These animals also reproduce
asexually by fragmentation.

The bryozoans (or ectoprocts) live in both marine and
fresh water. Superficially they resemble colonial coelenterates and also have many different functional kinds of
individuals in the colony. Their reproductive methods
are extremely varied.

Although some bryozoans are either male or female, most
species are hermaphroditic. The gametes or sex cells develop from internal tissues, and fertilization of eggs takes
place mostly inside the body. They are among the few
hermaphroditic animals having species that self-fertilize
(rather than cross-fertilize), although in some species the
sperm develop long before the ova, so that self-fertilization
is prevented. Most eggs are brooded in a sac inside the
body, and free-living larvae are eventually released. After
some time, they settle down and produce a new colony.

Colonies of bryozoans develop by extensive asexual
budding from the original larva that settled down and
attached to some substrate. When the larva is brooded

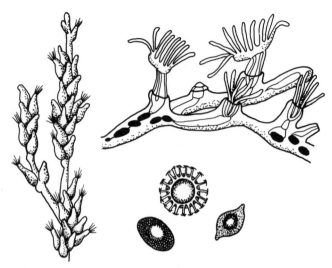

Figure 88.

Combination of reproductive methods in bryozoans: colony on the left formed by external budding; an enlarged view of part of colony (upper right) showing internal buds or stato-blasts (in black), and three different kinds of statoblasts.

inside an individual, there are cases where the developing cells of the embryo separate, so that considerable twinning (polyembryony) results from an original fertilized egg. Freshwater bryozoans also engage in a form of asexual reproduction by internal budding of statoblasts.

The annelids, or segmented worms, are related to the arthropods (of which insects are the largest subgroup). In annelids such as the clamworm, the sexes are separate and fertilization of eggs takes place in the water, followed by a free-living larva that eventually develops into a new worm. In hermaphroditic annelids such as earthworms and leeches, there is reciprocal cross-fertilization, and the young hatch out of cocoons.

While these sexual methods are the ones mostly used in reproductive activities of annelids, many species reproduce asexually by budding, fragmentation, and fission of the parent body. Regeneration of new parts follows these processes.

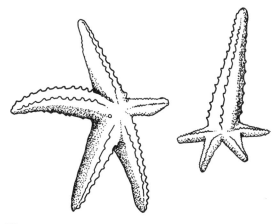

Figure 89.

Regeneration in starfish. An arm about half-regenerated (left figure), and a single detached arm which has regenerated four smaller arms (right figure).

The arthropods as a group have separate sexes, but there are some hermaphroditic subgroups. Although some have regenerative powers, asexual capabilities are mostly absent. Many have alternate methods of reproduction, however, including parthenogenesis in some crustaceans (cladocerans and ostracods) and in insects (plant lice, gall wasps, honeybees), as well as polyembryony in some of the insects.

The echinoderm group of invertebrates (which includes starfish, sea urchins, sand dollars, sea cucumbers) are almost exclusively either males or females and reproduce sexually by shedding eggs and sperm into the water. A larva forms from the fertilized egg and develops into an adult. However, there are many types in which asexual reproduction occurs by fragmenting or casting off parts which then regenerate into complete animals.

There are some minor groups of invertebrates which show certain kinds of kinship with the vertebrates. Among these are the tunicates, the most familiar of which are the sea squirts. Although these animals are hermaphroditic, cross-fertilization is the rule. In addition, the tunicates reproduce by budding, and also have the capacity to regenerate lost parts.

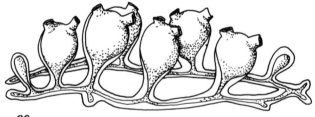

Figure 90.

A colony of sea squirts or tunicates. Although these hermaphroditic animals cross-fertilize, they also reproduce asexually by budding.

Epilogue

WHILE invertebrate animals have been considered as individuals in this book, in nature they really exist as populations, in which a certain number of individuals occupy a given area at a given time. All populations of animals have certain characteristics, such as density, varied age groups, and birth and death rates. The density of invertebrates can be enormous—for example, a million protozoa in a quart of water, or several million insects of a given species on an acre of land. The smaller the animal, generally the more dense it is.

If any species of animal were to reproduce in an unlimited fashion, it would overrun the earth. A single tapeworm may lay 100,000 eggs per day and an oyster 60,000,000 eggs in a season, yet all animal intestines are not afflicted with tapeworms, and the edge of the sea is not choked with oysters. There are a variety of regulatory factors that do not permit the development of all these eggs, such as food supply limits, competition with other species for space, predation, and decrease in reproductive frequency because of crowded conditions. Each population of animals reaches an equilibrium—a saturation level—beyond which increases in density do not occur. Even though some populations are relatively stable from year to year, most undergo considerable fluctuations on a seasonal basis.

As the human animal has evolved, it has not only domesticated itself to the danger point but has also developed total dependency on farm and ranch animals and domesticated grain crops. The quantity of cattle, hogs, sheep, chickens, wheat, rice, corn, and barley needed to maintain the present human population cannot be produced without human management, and even at that, production cannot keep up with demand. Along with this, the landings of fish and shellfish are on a decline, and the world has a critical food shortage which promises to become ever more acute in the years ahead.

With the apparent dwindling supplies of traditional food, it is not a wild notion that the dietary habits of people will have to be modified. The farming and eating of non-backboned animals that are not presently found on any menu may well have to be considered. If such a day ever comes, the reproductive habits of non-backboned animals will become an increasingly important area of study as it will have a more direct application to human needs and survival.

GLOSSARY

SUGGESTED READING

INDEX

Glossary

asexual reproduction. The production of offspring from a single
parent; the offspring are genetic copies.

autogamy. Self-fertilization, a form of sexual reproduction in which
there is genetic recombination within the same individual.

binary fission. Asexual reproduction in which the parent produces
two offspring of equal size.

budding. A type of asexual reproduction in which offspring grow
from the parent.

cloaca. A receptacle found in many animals into which digestive,
excretory, and reproductive ducts empty.

coelom. The body cavity of animals.

colonial protozoa. Protozoa which live as aggregates of single cells.

conjugation. A form of sexual reproduction in ciliates, in which
two individuals come together temporarily and exchange genetic
material.

cyst. A stage in the life cycle of an animal in which it is enclosed
in a protective envelope.

egg. A female gamete or sex cell.

fertilization. The fusion of sperm and egg nuclei to form a zygote.

fission. A form of asexual reproduction in which the parent divides
into two or more offspring identical to itself.

fragmentation. A form of asexual reproduction in which an animal
breaks up into several parts which then regenerate into offspring.

gamete. A sex cell, either an egg or a sperm.

gemmule. Internal buds of sponges.

gonad. A gland which produces either male or female sex gametes:
the ovary or testis.

hermaphroditism. The presence of both male and female gonads in the same animal.

hologomy. A process in protozoans in which the whole animal functions as a sex cell or gamete.

intersex. A condition in which a single animal exhibits male and female characteristics at the same time.

invertebrate. Any animal which lacks a backbone.

larva. An immature stage of an animal which changes drastically before becoming an adult.

life cycle. The entire life span of an animal from conception.

longitudinal binary fission. Binary fission in which the divisional plane is along the length of the animal.

multiple fission. Fission in which more than two offspring are produced from one parent.

oblique binary fission. Binary fission in which the divisional plane is at an angle to the length of the animal.

organ. A group of tissues which perform one or more functions.

ova. Eggs, or female gametes.

ovary. The female gonad which produces eggs.

ovotestis. A sex gland which produces both eggs and sperm.

paedogenesis. A type of asexual reproduction in which larvae produce more larvae.

parthenogenesis. The production of offspring from unfertilized eggs.

penis. The male organ which delivers sperm to the female animal.

photosynthesis. The manufacture of organic materials by green plants in the presence of light.

plasmotomy. A type of asexual reproduction in some protozoa, in which multinucleated organisms divide into several offspring.

polyembryony. A type of asexual reproduction in which several offspring develop from a single fertilized egg: twinning.

polymorphism. Different body forms in members of the same species.

protandry. A condition in which the same gonad produces first sperm, and then eggs.

regeneration. Regrowth of lost or injured parts of an animal.

reproduction. The process whereby an animal produces offspring.

schizogony. Multiple fission in the asexual phase of the life cycle of an animal.

sexual reproduction. The production of offspring from two parents; the offspring are a genetic combination of the parents.

spawning. The shedding of eggs and sperm into water for reproductive purposes.

species. An interbreeding population of animals.

sperm. A male gamete or sex cell.

spermatophore. A packaged collection of male gametes or sperm.

sporogony. Multiple fission which is preceded by sexual fertilization.

statoblast. Internal buds of bryozoans.

testis. The male gonad which produces sperm.

tissue. A group of similar cells performing a specific function.

transverse binary fission. Binary fission in which the divisional plane is across the length of the animal.

vagina. The female canal which receives sperm from the penis during copulation.

vertebrate. An animal with a backbone (fishes, amphibians, reptiles, birds, and mammals).

zygote. A fertilized egg.

Suggested Reading

FOR THE GENERAL READER

Berrill, J. J. *Sex and the Nature of Things.* New York: Dodd, Mead & Co., 1953.

Jenkins, M. M. *Animals Without Parents.* New York: Holiday House, 1970.

Keller, D. K. *Sex and the Single Cell.* New York: Pegasus, 1972.

Michelmore, S. *Sexual Reproduction.* New York: The Natural History Press, 1965.

Vorontsova, M., and Liosner, L. D. *Asexual Propagation and Regeneration.* New York: Pergamon Press, 1960.

Wendt, H. *The Sex Life of the Animals.* New York: Simon & Schuster, 1965.

FOR THE ADVANCED READER

Barnes, R. D. *Invertebrate Zoology.* Philadelphia: W. B. Saunders Co., 1974.

Gardner, M. S. *The Biology of Invertebrates.* New York: McGraw-Hill Book Co., 1972.

Hickman, C. P. *Biology of the Invertebrates.* St. Louis: C. V. Mosby Co., 1973.

Hyman, L. H. *The Invertebrates,* 6 vols. New York: McGraw-Hill Book Co., 1940–1967.

Meglitsch, P. A. *Invertebrate Zoology.* New York: Oxford University Press, 1972.

Index

(boldface numbers indicate illustrations)

113